COUNTRY GARDENS

Professional hints & tips for colouring

1 Before you start

To colour up a drawing properly you need to be well prepared. Sit upright with a straight back and posture. Work in natural light or beneath a good light source, but not in direct sunlight. Choose a flat or slightly angled surface to work on. Remove a page from your book and secure it to your surface with tape to prevent it from slipping. You can use either traditional coloured pencils, any water-based paints, or colouring pencils that can be mixed with water to create watercolour effects. Keep a cloth and eraser handy in case you need to make any changes. You are now ready to start.

2 Applying colour

There are many ways to paint a picture – over time you will develop your own method. Taking the front cover image as an example, a good place to start is the background. Blues are 'cold' colours and drop back whereas reds and oranges are 'warm' colours and jump forward. Also, light shades drop back and darker shades come forward. You can research the colour of the main subjects and background details by referring to books and following the colours accurately, or you can make them up as you go. Use broader areas of colour for the background first and add the details of colour and shadow later. The foreground subjects should be darker and stronger than the background.

3 Finishing off

Once you have painted your picture, stand back and look to see if there are parts that need a bit more work and that it all comes together. It is sometimes better to 'under work' than 'over work' a picture as it may end up being 'muddy' and confused. Let your painting dry out and be careful not to smudge coloured pencils. Keep finished pictures stored safely in a flat folder. If you are pleased with the result, why not get it framed so that it can be admired by family and friends!